Beginning Sounds

PRESCHOOL SKILLS

Illustrations by Nathan Jarvis

FlashKids™

Cover illustration by Nathan Jarvis

Flash Kids
122 Fifth Avenue
New York, NY 10011

ISBN: 978-1-4114-9950-8

Please submit all inquiries to FlashKids@bn.com

Printed and bound in China

Dear Parent,

Help your child build a solid foundation for reading and writing with this Preschool Skills workbook. Colorful illustrations and fun activities introduce basic beginning letter sounds. Help your child make the most of this workbook with these tips:

- Provide a quiet, comfortable place for your child to complete this workbook. Go through each page with him or her slowly to ensure full comprehension of each activity.

- If your child answers a question incorrectly, explain why it is incorrect and allow your child to correct the mistake.

- Encourage your child to ask questions and have discussions about the things your child finds interesting in this book. You can also ask your child questions to keep him or her engaged in learning.

- Try to relate concepts found in this book to things your child encounters in everyday life. For example, have your child identify letter sounds in familiar words—household objects, family members' names, and street signs.

- Most of all, enjoy this special time spent together! Reading to your child and helping him or her learn will build a strong bond between you both.

Dancing Ducks

Duck begins with the **D** sound. Circle all the things in the picture that **begin** with the **D** sound.

Circle the thing in each row that **begins** with the **same** sound as the first one.

harmonica

hammer

nail

saw

piano

apple

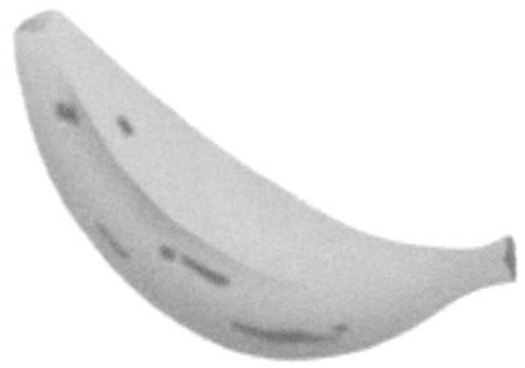
banana

pineapple

drum

cat

dog

mouse

guitar

flower

tree

grass

Draw a line to match the things that **begin** with the **same** sound.

fox

dog

ostrich

hippo

duck

fish

hamster

octopus

Goat in the Grass

Goat begins with the **G** sound.
Circle all the things in the picture
that **begin** with the **G** sound.

Monkey begins with the **M** sound. Help the monkey find its mother.

What letter did you make?

Cross out the things that
do not begin with the **P** sound.

penguin

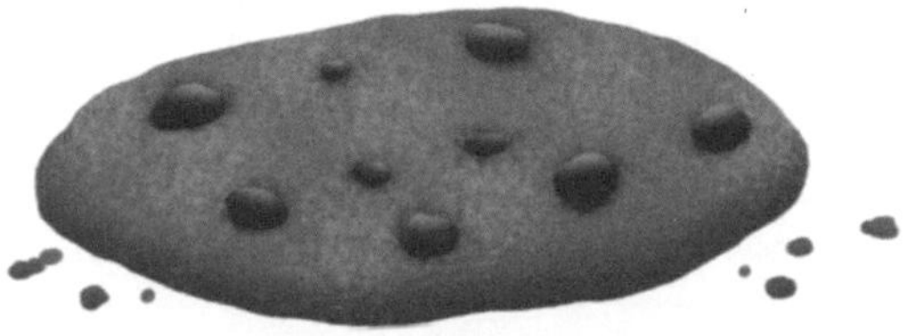

cookie

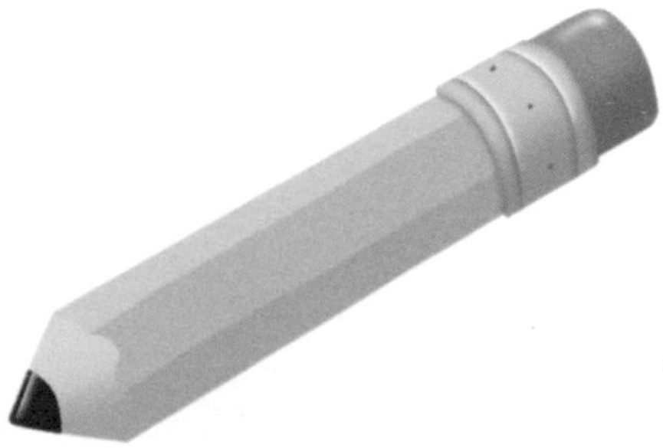

pencil

book

pear

peach

Circle the thing in each row that **begins** with the **same** sound as the first one.

 lion	 chair	 lamp	 bed
 monkey	 mirror	 brush	 comb
 kangaroo	 watch	 key	 purse
 zebra	 button	 pocket	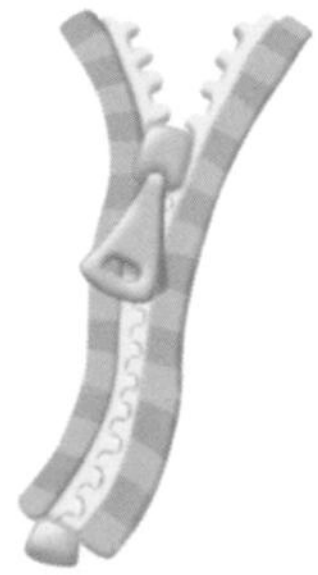 zipper

Kicky Kangaroo

Kangaroo begins with the **K** sound. Circle all the things in the picture that **begin** with the **K** sound.

Draw a line to match the things that **begin** with the **same** sound.

boat

dominos

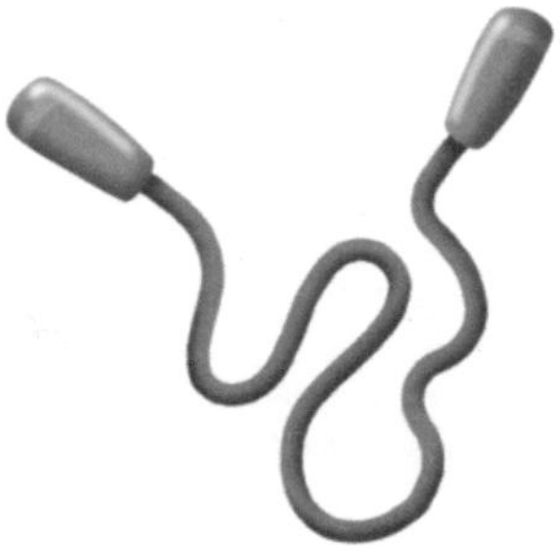

jump rope

truck

top

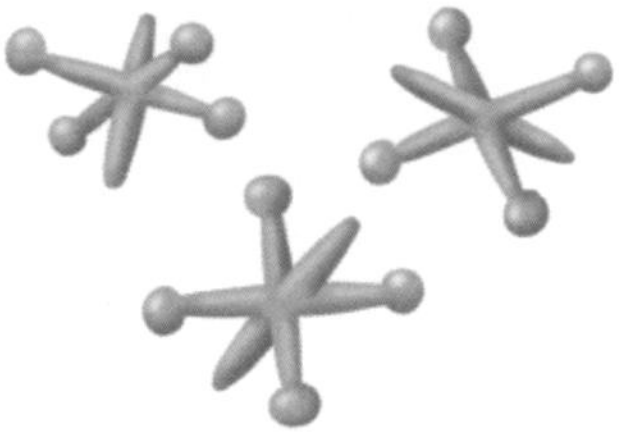

jacks

doll

bear

Circle the thing in each row that **begins** with the **same** sound as the first one.

 hat	 horse	 cow	 goat
 cake	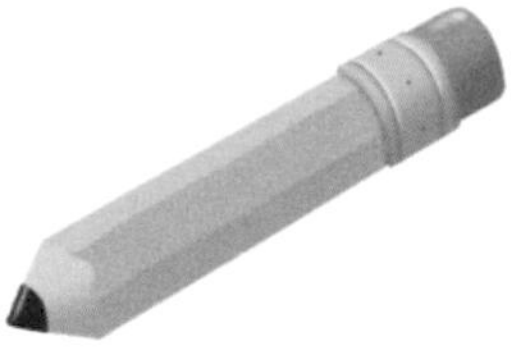 pencil	 car	 boat
 present	 truck	 book	 paintbrush
 balloon	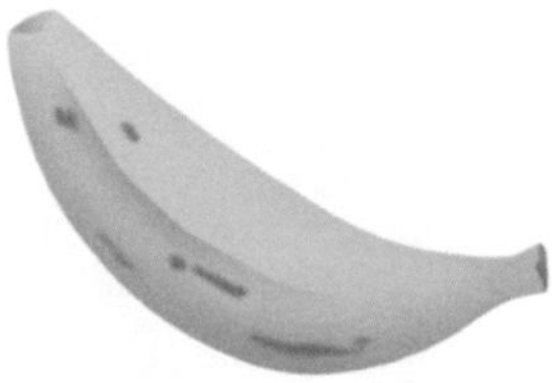 banana	 apple	 orange

Snake begins with the **S** sound.
Help the snake find the sun and sand.

What letter did you make?

Running in the Rain

Run begins with the **R** sound.
Circle all the things in the picture
that **begin** with the **R** sound.

Quiet begins with the **Q** sound.
Cross out the things that
do not begin with the **Q** sound.

queen

ring

quilt

duck

quarter

Draw a line to match the things that **begin** with the **same** sound.

cake

peach

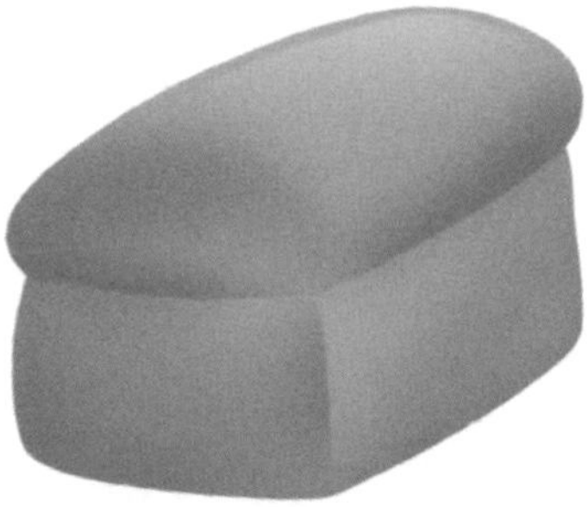

bread

juice

pie

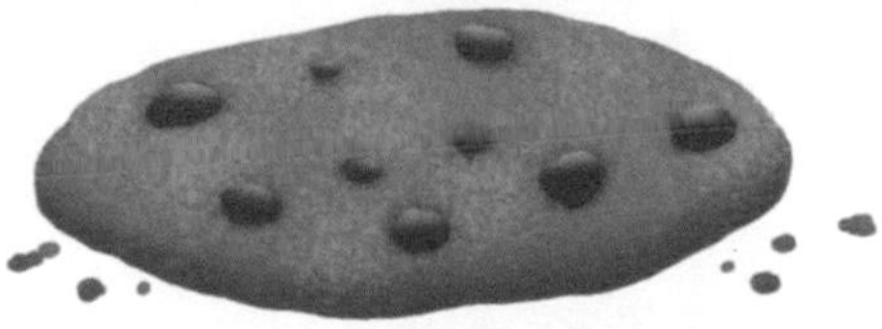

cookie

jelly

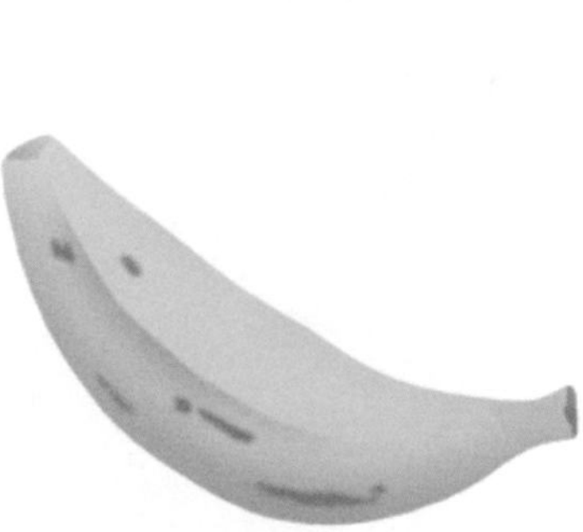

banana

Lion begins with the **L** sound.
Help the lion find its lunch.

What letter did you make?

Circle the thing in each row that **begins** with the **same** sound as the first one.

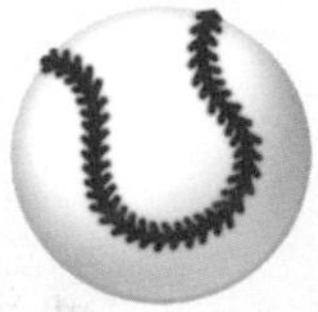 ball	 chicken	 mop	 broom
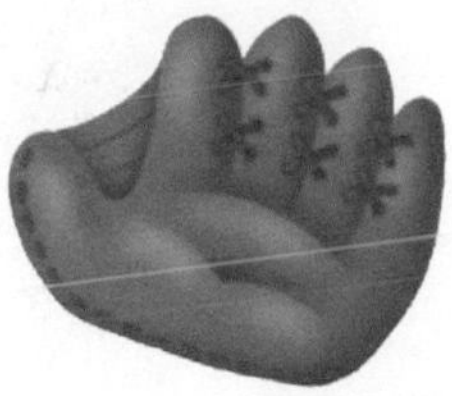 glove	 goat	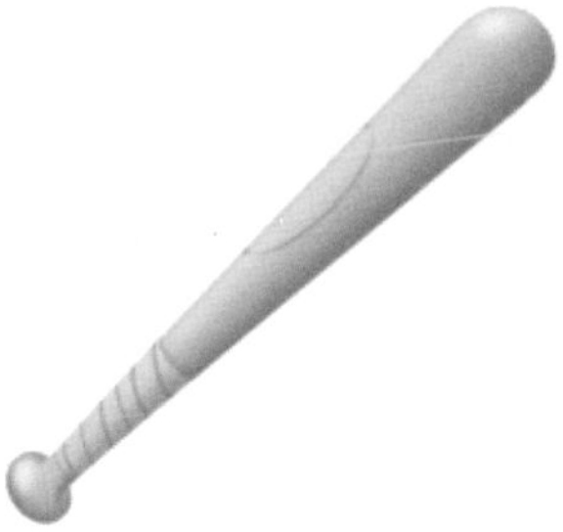 bat	 horse
 cap	 lettuce	 carrot	 pumpkin
 shoe	 shell	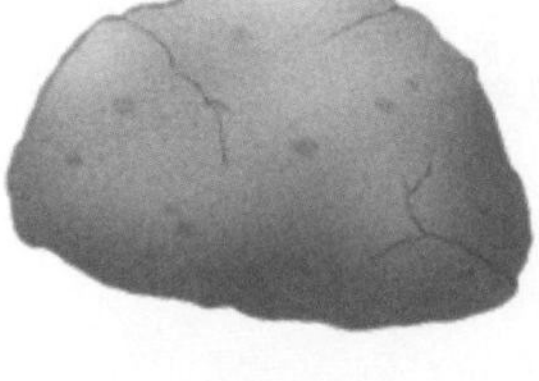 rock	 flower

Nest begins with the **N** sound.
Cross out the things that
do not begin with the **N** sound.

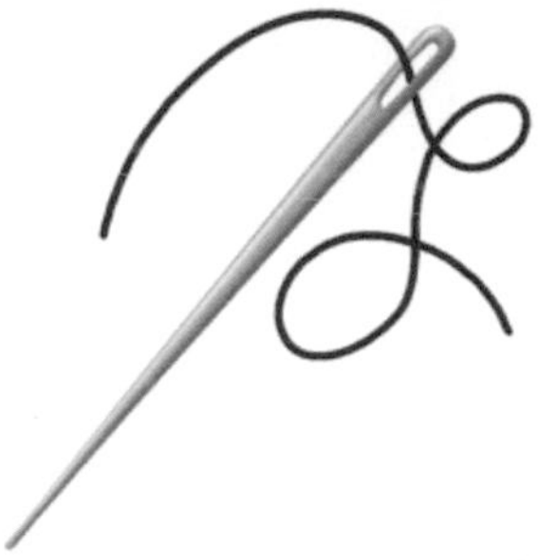

needle

vest

noodles

nut

monkey

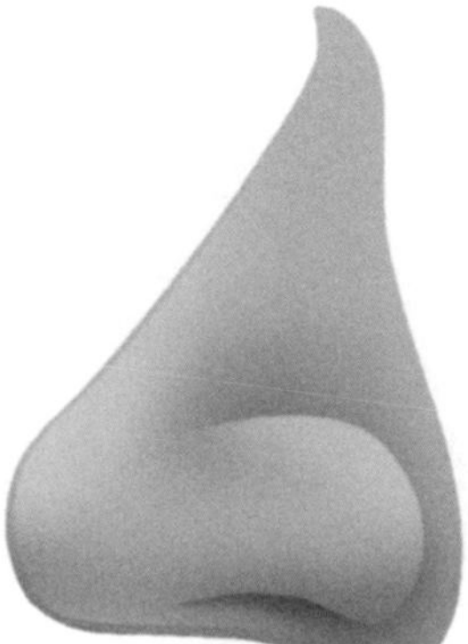

nose

In an Igloo

Igloo begins with the **I** sound.
Circle all the things in the picture that **begin** with the **I** sound.

Umbrella begins with the **U** sound.
Help Uncle Umberto find his umbrella.

What letter did you make?

Circle the thing in each row that **begins** with the **same** sound as the first one.

Alligator begins with the **A** sound.
Cross out the things that
do not begin with the **A** sound.

ant

apple

car

airplane

dog

ax

Draw a line to match the things that **begin** with the **same** sound.

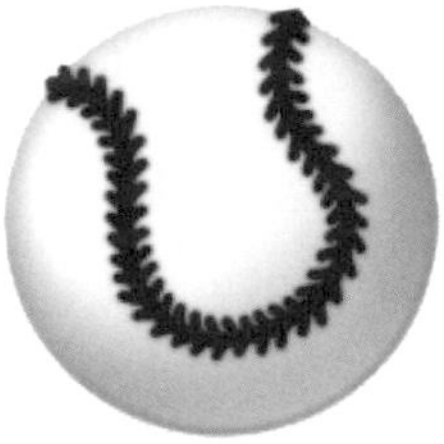

ball

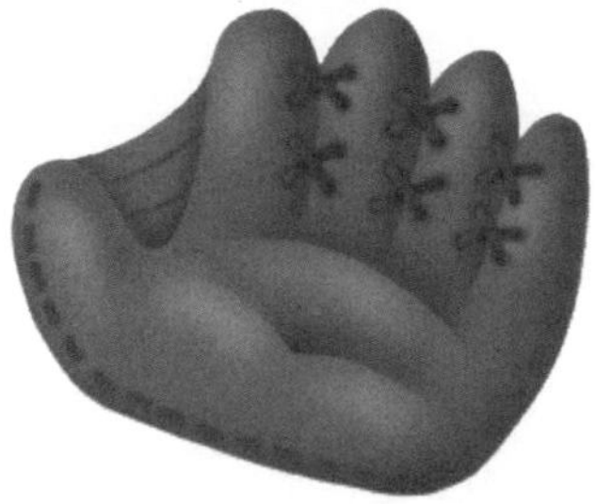

glove

helmet

shoe

skate

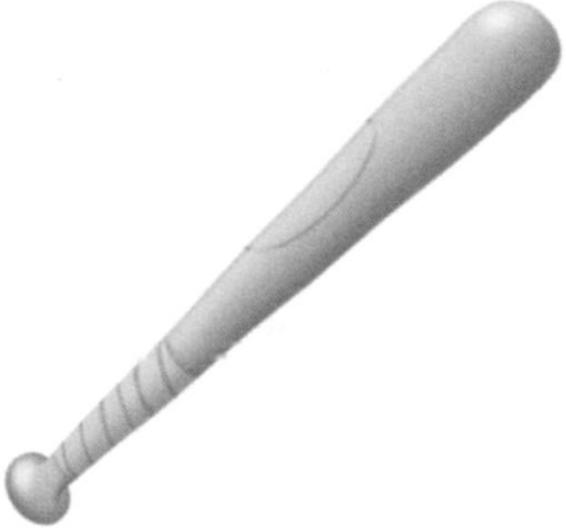

bat

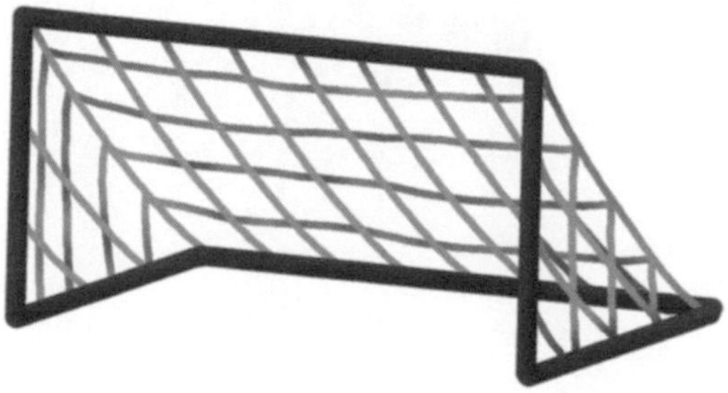

goal

hoop

Walrus begins with the **W** sound.
Help Walter Walrus find
his friend Wendy Whale.

What letter did you make?

Circle the thing in each row that **begins** with the **same** sound as the first one.

 bag	 lion	 tiger	 bear
 apple	 ant	 butterfly	 snail
 milk	 man	 baby	 girl
 sandwich	 flower	 tree	 sun

Time for T

Time begins with the **T** sound. Circle all the things in the picture that **begin** with the **T** sound.

Elbow begins with the **E** sound.
Cross out the things that
do not begin with the **E** sound.

egg

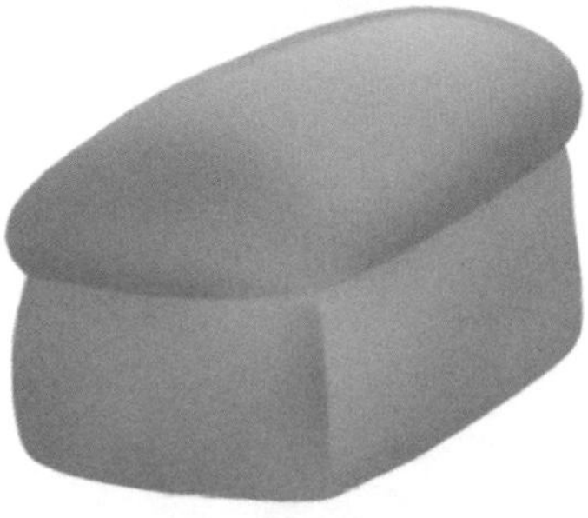

bread

elephant

elf

cow

eagle

Draw a line to match the things that **begin** with the **same** sound.

clown

car

tiger

juggle

popcorn

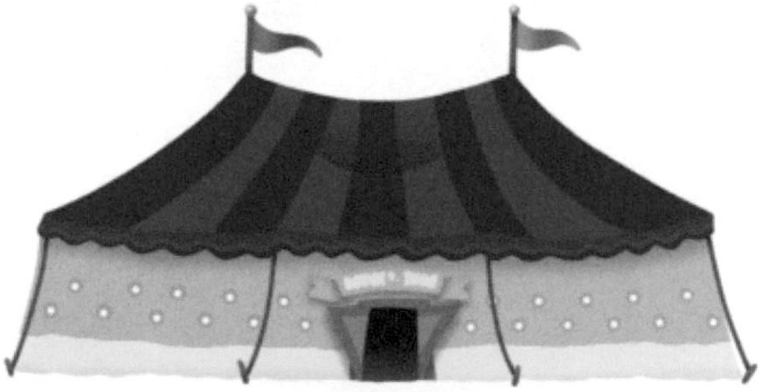

tent

jump

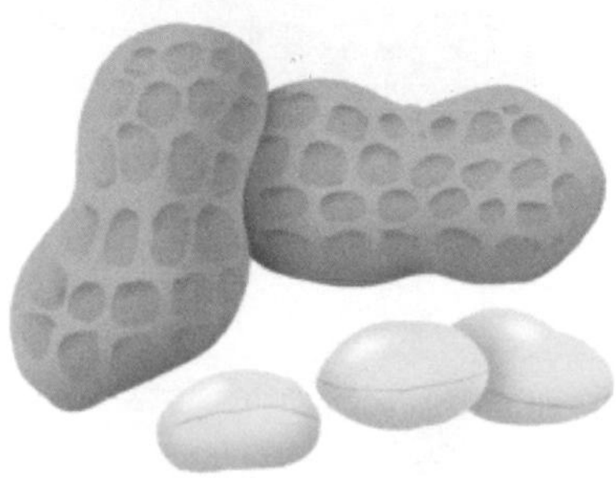

peanuts

Violin begins with the **V** sound.
Help Victor find his violin.

What letter did you make?

Circle the thing in each row that **begins** with the **same** sound as the first one.

 soap	 butterfly	 snail	 ladybug
 towel	 turtle	 frog	 snake
 duck	 seal	 dolphin	 crab
 robe	 bird	 cloud	 rainbow

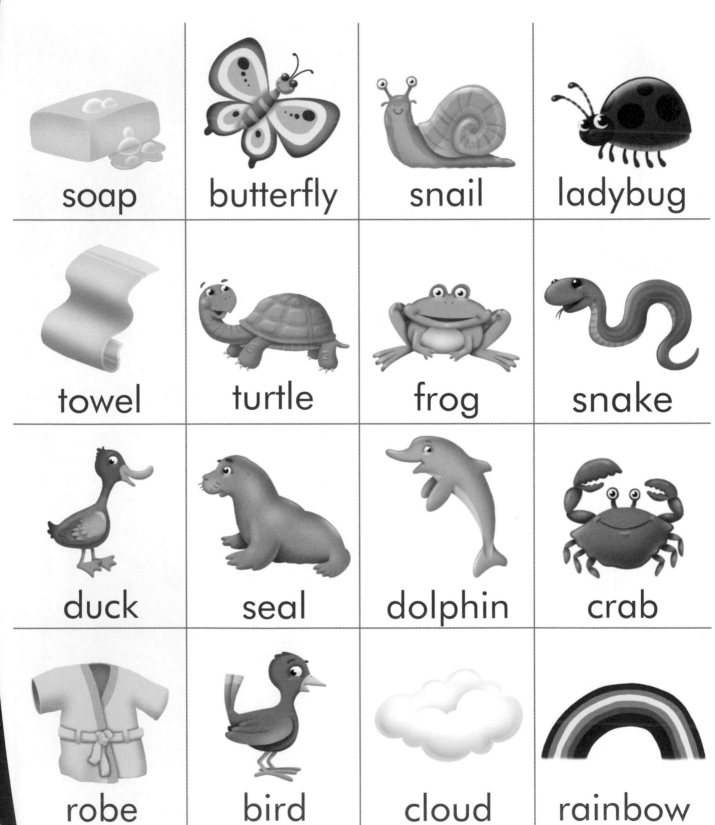

Yesterday begins with the **Y** sound.
Cross out the things that
do not begin with the **Y** sound.

yellow

fox

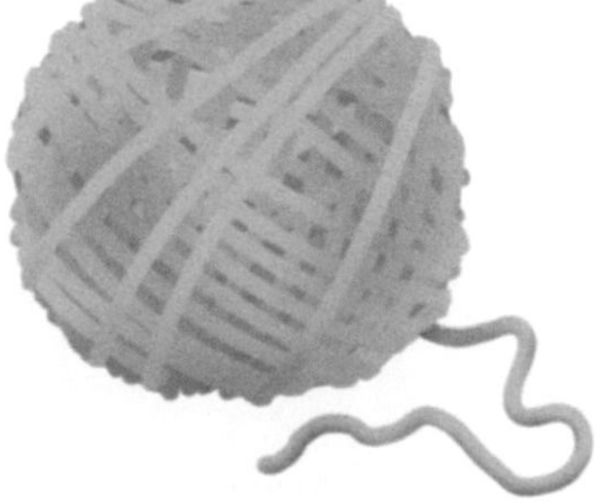

yarn

yak

doll

yo-yo

A Quiet Queen

Quiet begins with the **Q** sound.
Circle all the things in the picture
that **begin** with the **Q** sound.

Draw a line to match the things that **begin** with the **same** sound.

baby

doll

crib

cry

diaper

bottle

horse

hat

Circle the thing in each row that **begins** with the **same** sound as the first one.

 wheelbarrow	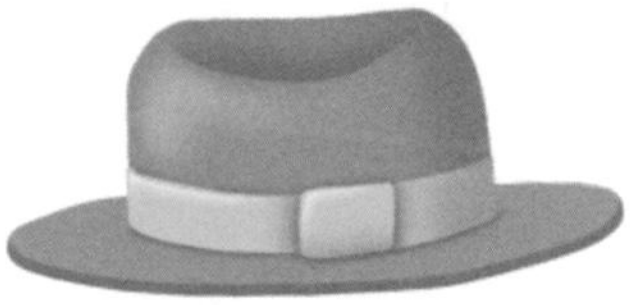 hat	 watch	 belt
 tomato	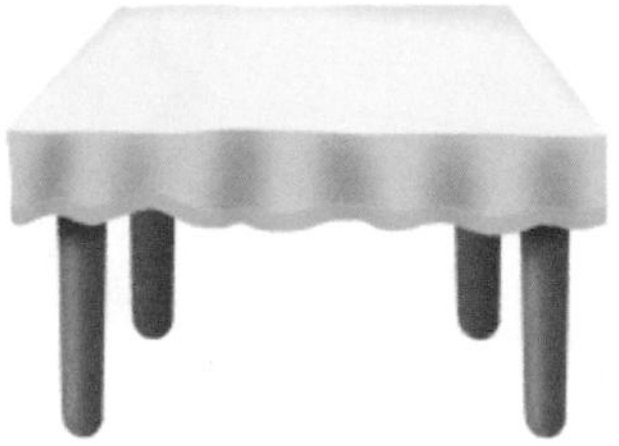 table	 chair	 rug
 lettuce	 grass	 flower	 leaf
 rabbit	 dress	 ring	 vest

Zebra begins with the **Z** sound.
Help the zebra find its way to the zoo.

What letter did you make?

Ostrich begins with the **o** sound.
Cross out the things that
do not begin with the **o** sound.

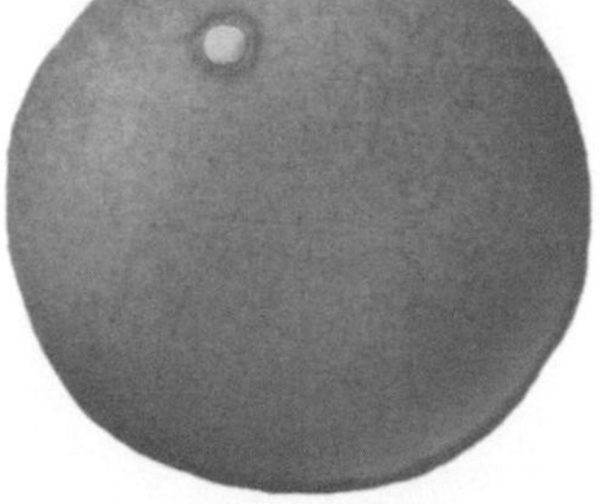

orange

otter

nest

octopus

tree

olive

A Fine Day

Fine begins with the **F** sound.
Circle all the things in the picture that **begin** with the **F** sound.

Draw a line to match the things that **begin** with the **same** sound.

shell

ball

bucket

family

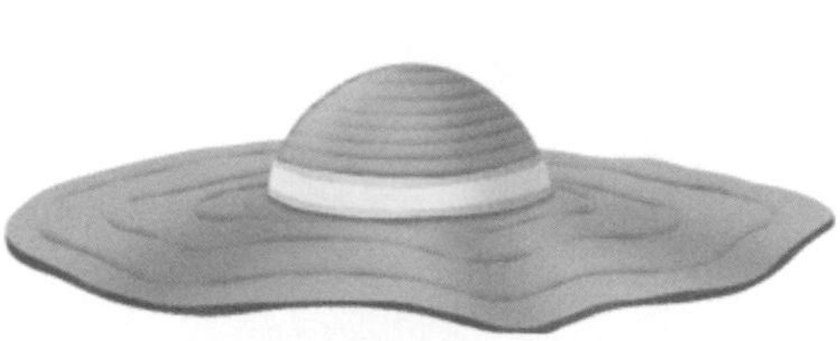

hat

sand

fish

hot

Circle the thing in each row that **begins** with the **same** sound as the first one.

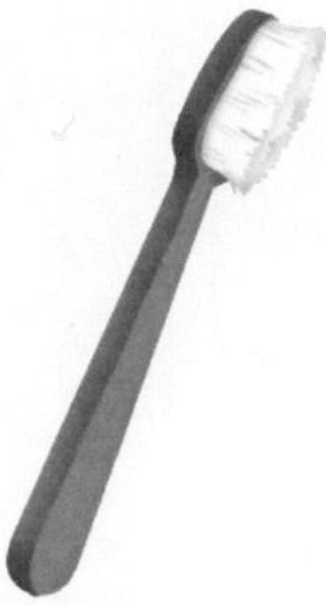 toothbrush	 lettuce	 tomato	 carrot
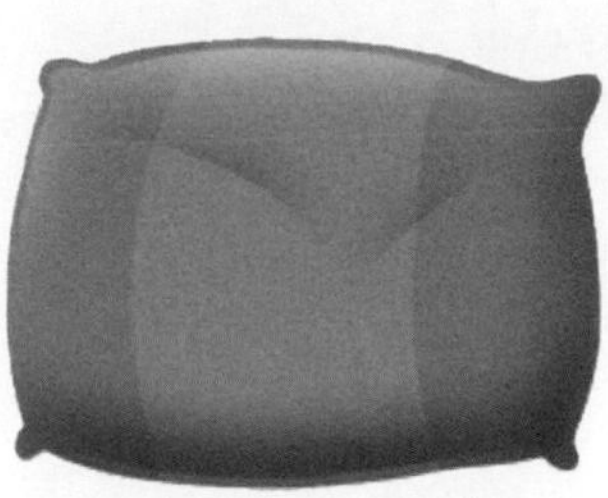 pillow	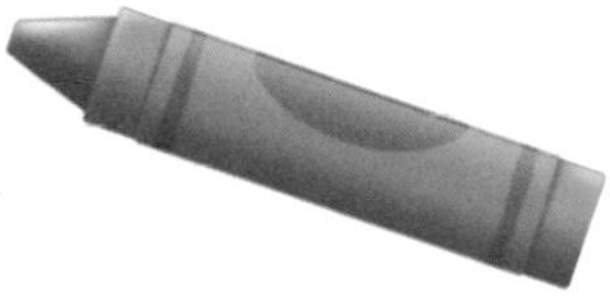 crayon	 book	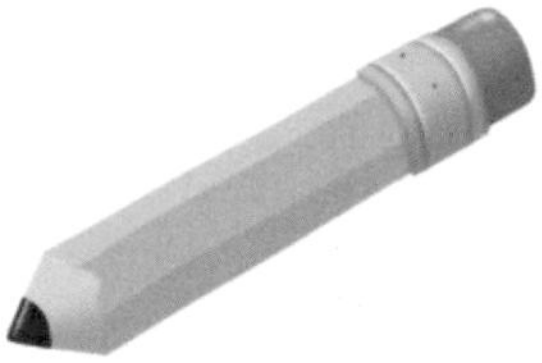 pencil
 blanket	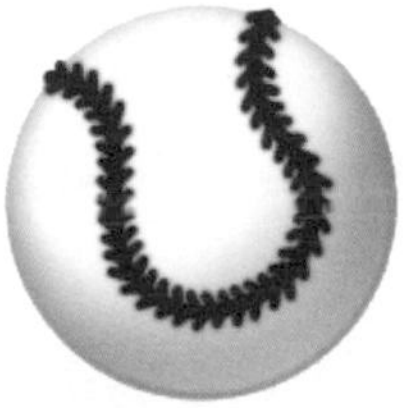 ball	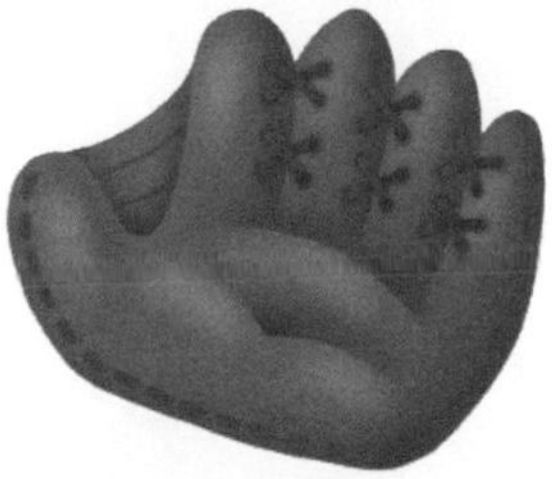 glove	 cap
 moon	 lion	 monkey	 tiger

Cat begins with the **C** sound.
Help the cat find the comfy couch.

What letter did you make?

Violet begins with the **V** sound.
Cross out the things that
do not begin with the **V** sound.

vest

bee

violin

valentine

broom

vacuum

What a Mess!

Mess begins with the **M** sound. Circle all the things in the picture that **begin** with the **M** sound.

Circle the thing in each row that **begins** with the **same** sound as the first one.

 turtle	 sun	 flower	 tree
 frog	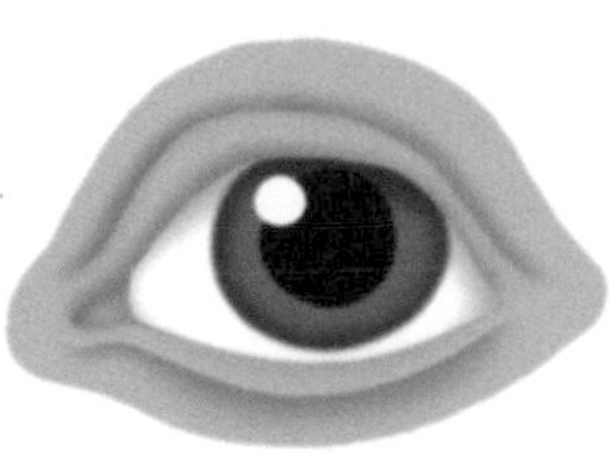 eye	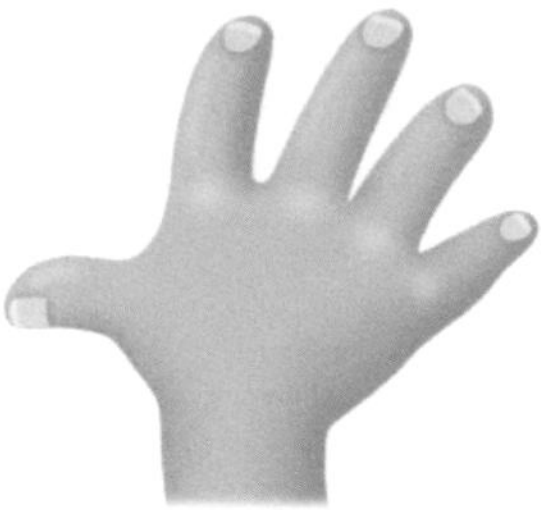 hand	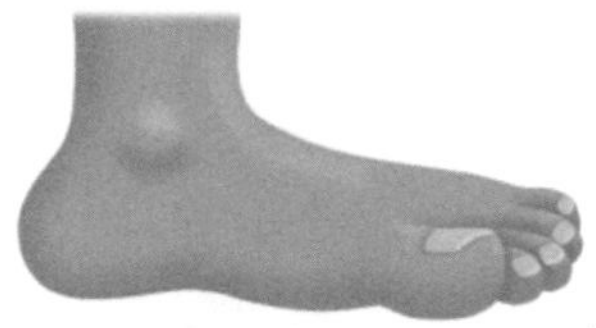 foot
 snake	 butterfly	 snail	 ladybug
 lizard	 lamp	 chair	 table

Say the name of each picture.
Write the **beginning** sound.

apple a

boat b

cat c

doll d

egg e

fish f

Say the name of each picture.
Write the **beginning** sound.

goat g

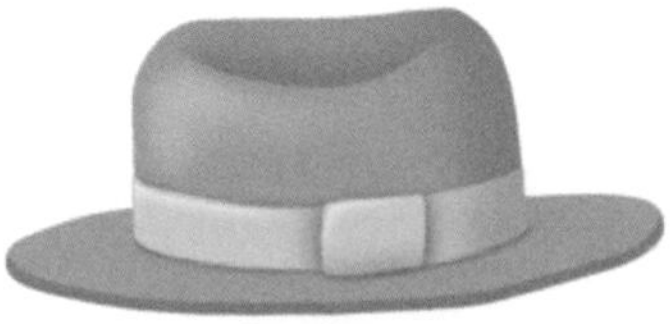

hat h

igloo i

jar j

key k

lamp l

Say the name of each picture.
Write the **beginning** sound.

moon m

nest n

octopus o

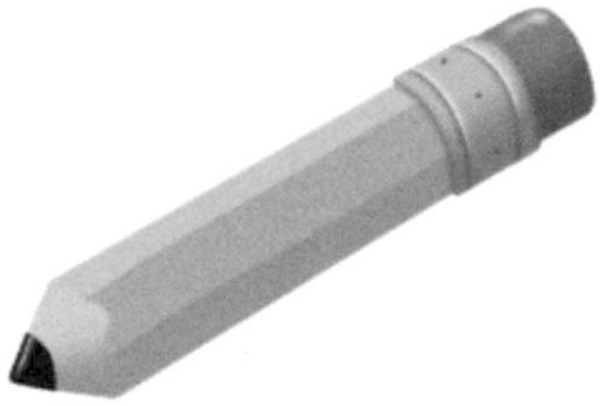

pencil p

quarter q

rake r

sun s

Say the name of each picture.
Write the **beginning** sound.

turtle t

umbrella u

violin v

whale w

xylophone x

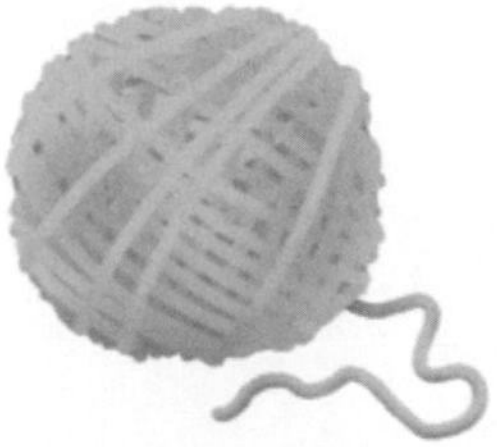

yarn y

zebra z

Draw a line from each picture to its **beginning** sound.

N

I

E

L

Draw a line from each picture to its **beginning** sound.

W

A

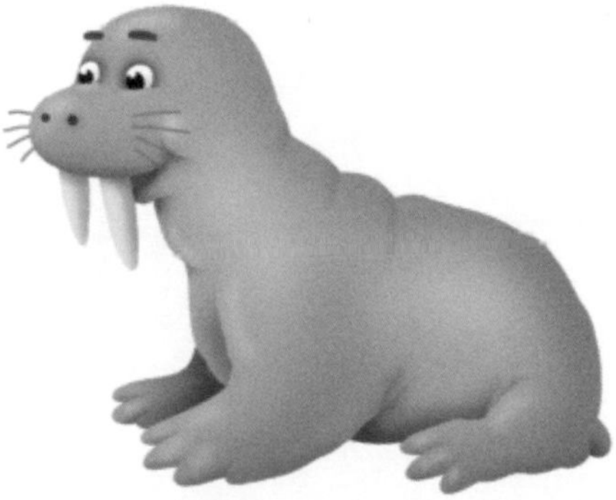

Z

K

Draw a line from each picture to its **beginning** sound.

X

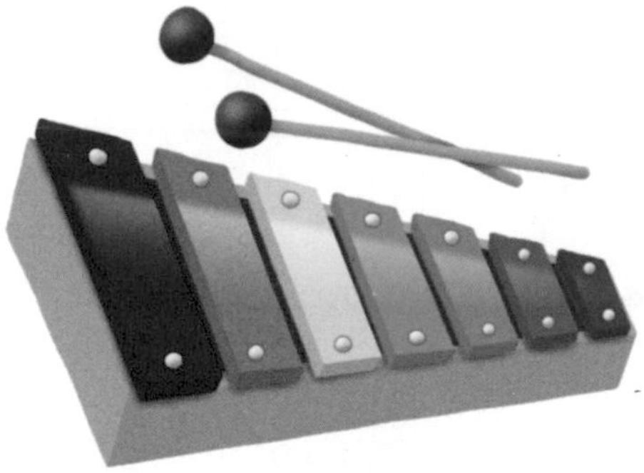

P

G

V

Draw a line from each picture to its **beginning** sound.

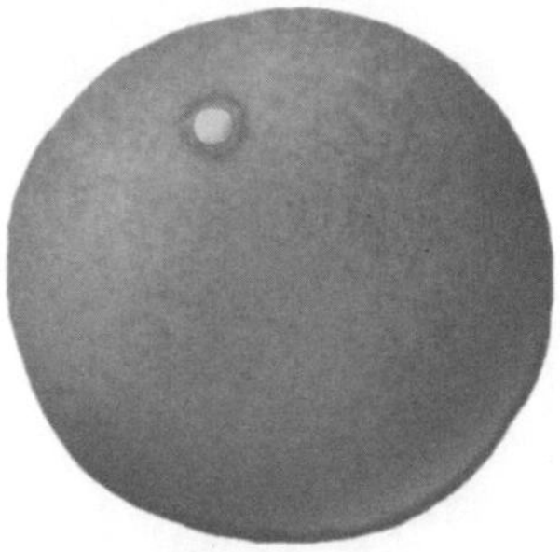

A

B

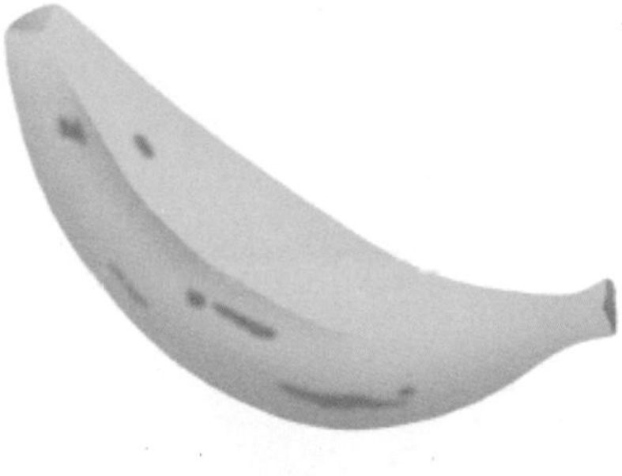

S

O

Cross out the thing in each row that **does not begin** with the letter sound shown.

H

I

K

O

Cross out the thing in each row that **does not begin** with the letter sound shown.

Q

U

Y

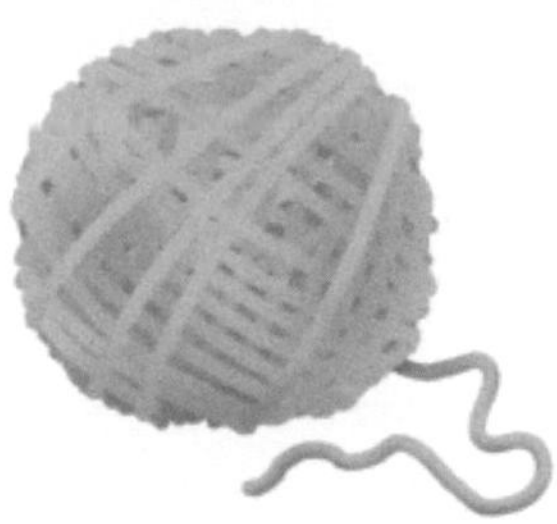

R

Cross out the thing in each row that **does not begin** with the letter sound shown.

T

F

D

C

Cross out the thing in each row that **does not begin** with the letter sound shown.

J

M

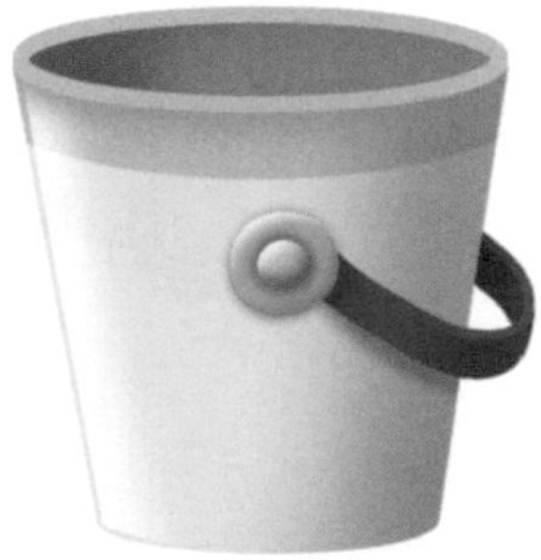

L

N

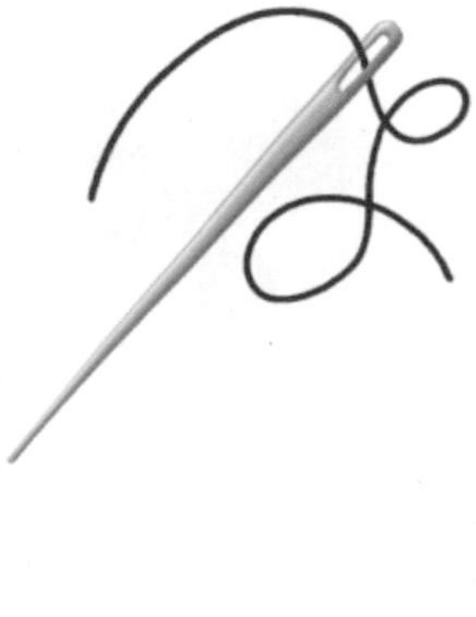

Circle the letter that makes the **beginning** sound for each picture.

boat

a b c

train

r s t

car

c d e

airplane

a b c

Circle the letter that makes the **beginning** sound for each picture.

fish

f g h

octopus

n o p

whale

u v w

dolphin

c d e

Circle the letter that makes the **beginning** sound for each picture.

tree

r s t

nest

n o p

bird

b c d

worm

v w x

Circle the letter that makes the **beginning** sound for each picture.

shoes

s t u

hat

g h i

jacket

h i j

pants

o p q

Circle the letter that makes the **beginning** sound for each picture.

cow

a b c

goat

f g h

duck

d e f

mouse

l m n

Circle the letter that makes the **beginning** sound for each picture.

vacuum

t u v

mop

m n o

broom

a b c

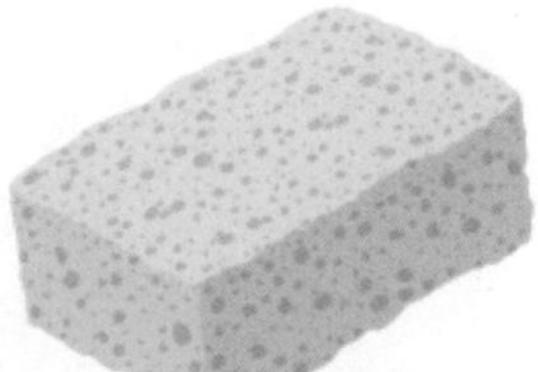

sponge

s t u

Good work,

_________________________________ !

(Name)

You are ready to read!